GAMES
CALCULATORS
PLAY

can make your calculator play
a bigger role in your life!

Play along with GAMES CALCULATORS
PLAY and you'll win a prize you never expected.
After you've done a number of the games and
tricks in this book, you'll find you're handling
the math in your school, business and daily life
with greater skill. You'll know how your calculator operates, how to think ahead to make it
do more for you and how to analyze your problems so that your calculator can solve them.
The GAMES CALCULATORS PLAY can be an
interesting education.

GAMES
CALCULATORS
PLAY

by Wallace Judd

WARNER BOOKS

A Warner Communications Company

WARNER BOOKS EDITION

Copyright © 1975 by Wallace Judd
All rights reserved.

ISBN 0-446-84434-9

Cover design by Gene Light

Cover photograph by The New Studio

Text design by Milton Batalion

Photographs on pages 35 and 38 by John Dexter

Illustrations by Karen McCracken

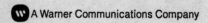 A Warner Communications Company

Warner Books, Inc., 75 Rockefeller Plaza, New York, N.Y. 10019

Printed in the United States of America

Not associated with Warner Press, Inc. of Anderson, Indiana

10   9   8   7   6   5   4

*This book is dedicated
to Ray Haas—
in gratitude for the start
he gave me in the field of
mathematics writing.*

CONTENTS

GAMES
CALCULATORS
PLAY

INTRODUCTION

This little book is intended to let you unlock the fun that exists in your calculator. By giving you a few clues about how to play with your calculator, I hope the book will not only increase your enjoyment of the machine, but give you some genuine insights into numbers as well.

Learning the games your calculator can play is not without benefit. After you do a number of the games and tricks in this book, you'll probably be able to handle your accounting and math problems with greater ease than before.

If you need some very basic clues on operating your calculator, turn to the chapter headed "How To..." and read it. It tells you how to use your constant key, how to change fractions to decimals, and how to do percents. When you're comfortable with your calculator, then move up front to the amusement park, and begin.

You will notice in the text that numbers with four or more digits do not have commas, just as calculators do not have commas. This avoids the possibility of mistaking a comma for a decimal point. Long numbers are printed with spaces every three digits to help you read them. For example, the number 4093847 is written 4 093 847, so it is obvious at a glance that it's seven digits long. Long decimals are treated in the same way. The number .000 007 is substantially easier to read and key in than .000007. For the latter, one practically needs to point at each of the zeros while counting them.

If your calculator has arithmetic logic instead of the more popular algebraic logic, some of the solutions may have to be keyed differently on your machine. An arithmetic logic calculator has combined function keys of plus-equals and minus-equals, while the algebraic logic calculator has separate keys for plus, minus, and equals. All the problems and solutions in this book can be done on an arithmetic calculator, but any variation in key function should be borne in mind.

This book just hints at the many, many possibilities for exploring numbers with the calculator. You'll find that number patterns are delightfully easy to conjure up, if you try. The fascinating relationships hidden in the numbers on clocks and calendars and time-schedules begin to emerge after a little investigation with the calculator. And problems of pollution, population, as well as the economics of daily living become more manageable and immediate with the aid of an electronic brain at your fingertips.

Have fun. Enjoy the numbers. Even more, enjoy what's beyond them.

Wallace Judd
March 19, 1975
Palo Alto, Calif.

P.S. You will find solutions to the problems that require them in the back of the book beginning on page 111.

NUMBER NAMES

Calculator trivia quiz

For the insignificant answers to these insignificant questions, simply compute the problems on your calculator, then stand on your head (or turn the calculator over).

Where was Napoleon's last domain?

$1234 \times 5 - 2552 + 255 =$

What famous author wrote *Siddhartha?*

$170 \times 200 + 1534 =$

What singing group sang *How Can I Make It Without You?*

$(3 \times 3 \div 100 \times 3 - .001) \times 3 =$

What did the queen hide behind her fan as the emperor walked by in his new clothes?

A _____

To fill in the blank: $47.5 \times 2 \times 20 \times 200 - 81 =$

When Gloria Glamorson was asked what her formula for success in the movie industry was. She answered:

"$202 \times 41 + 5 \times 7 - .082 =$"

So, you thought it was SHELL OIL that was at the root of the gas crisis. But at the Shell research grounds, they have come up with another formulation that takes Shell out of the picture. Their analysis:

$203 \times 7 + .8279 \div 2 - $ SHELL.OIL $=$ the culprit

(To subtract SHELL.OIL, subtract 710.77345.)

Close on the trail of his suspect, Bond landed at a remote airfield near Point Barrow, Alaska. As his eyes scanned the trackless, frozen horizon, 007 knew where to look. He followed these directions and found the astonished suspect inside:

$.6 \times .2 - .007 \times .7 =$

When Tim Callard, the perennially late salesman, walked through the door, he was hungry for dinner. His wife tabulated the 2693 seconds he was late, times the 13 times he'd promised before and failed—then added 1 for forgiveness but subtracted .486 for getting even. Computing these on her calculator, she showed him what was cooked for dinner.

Mr. Johnson, a rumpled old math teacher, was a rather crotchety sort. So, when he told his students they could make up their own problems for the calculator, Melinda made the best of the situation.

She did: $(323 \times 25) + .14 =$

What did Mr. Johnson read as he walked in front of her desk and looked at her calculator?

But why just settle for words or phrases?

After each equal sign below, write in the word that appears on your calculator.

We did an example for you:

$$69 \times 5 = \text{5hE}$$

$$+ \ 57\ 390 = \text{5ELL5}$$

$$- \ 56\ 817 = \text{BIG}$$

$$+ \ 576\ 427 = \text{5hELL5}$$

How does Charlie Chaplin prepare his dinner in *The Gold Rush*?

17×2	=
$+ \ 57\ 074$	=
$- \ 56\ 594$	=
$+ \ 2531$	=
$\div \ 6090$	=
$\times \ 1028$	=
$+ \ 3191$	=
$- \ 3654$	=
$+ \ 34\ 956$	=

TRICKS

Tricks to play on others (and your calculator)

Before you look for your victim, put into your calculator 18 181 818 + 13 131 313

Make sure you don't push the = key.

Now you're loaded for bear.

Walk up to a friend, and tell him or her that you have a special number in the calculator. Just ask your pal to look at the number that's on the display, and then push equals.

Instantaneously, the digits will switch,

from **13 13 13 13**

to **31 31 31 31**

Another variation is to ask somebody if he has a favorite digit. If not, ask him to pick one.

Make sure your calculator is on constant. Then, so he can see you—but not so slowly that he can follow you—key in:

$$0 \div .9 =$$

Now, tell him to push his favorite digit (just one), and then the equal sign.

Watch his face light up as the readout lights up with his digit all across it.

For example, if you do $0 \div .9 =$ first and then push 7 =, the display will read:

7. 7 7 7 7 7 7 7

To do the same thing with two digits, just put in 0×1 010 101 = (make sure the calculator is on constant). Then ask the person to pick his lucky two-digit number. When he pushes the two digits and equals, his number will light up like a Broadway marquee.

For example, if you do:
(constant on)
0×1 010 101 =
and your friend inputs 38 =
the display will read:

38383838

How to make your calculator count

Some people say that machines are dumb—but your calculator can count.

To show these machine-snubbing snobs the potential of your mini-calculator simply:
    making sure your machine is on constant
    putting in 10 000 000
    multiplying by 1.000 000 1
    pressing equals lots of times.

Your machine will "count" with the numbers on the right-hand side!!!

Can you figure out how to make your machine count by 5's? by 7's? by 3's? by any number? It can!

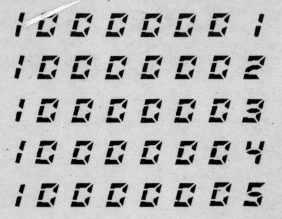

But Can It Count Backwards?

The answer is yes! I'll show you how to make it count backwards by 2's. You figure out how to make it count backwards by 1's.

To count backwards by 2's, be sure your calculator is on constant. Then:
Enter 10 000 200
multiply by .999 999 9
push equals lots of times.

It'll count *backwards* by 2's.

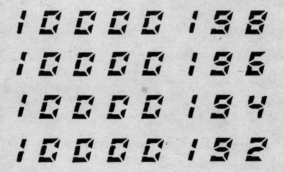

GAMES

The game of 21

If you didn't bring your deck of cards with you, you can still play the game of 21 on your calculator.

Just limit yourself and the other player to the keys 1, 2, and 3. On each turn you can push only one of the three keys—along with the + key.

The first person to reach 21 is the winner.

For example:	Readout
First player tries 2 +	2
Second player counters with 3 +	5
First player sticks to 2 +	7
Second player retreats to 1 +	8
First player boldly tries 3 +	11
Second player bets on 2 +	13
First player squirms with 1 +	14
Second player triumphantly pushes 3 +	17
First player (beaten) plays 1 +	18
Second player finishes it off with 3 +	21

If it is too easy to win at that, then play to 50 using the keys 1, 2, 3, 4, 5, and 6. Same rules apply.

Over and Under

This game is like the games on the previous page—except that now the keys don't go in sequence. You try to get to 21, but play with the keys 1, 4, and 7. Now you again take turns pressing a key and the symbol, except this time if you go over 21 you have to subtract. When you go back below 21 you have to add. The game goes on until somebody wins, or a standoff is declared.

Here's a sample game:			**Readout**
First	7 +		**7**
	Second	4 +	**11**
First	7 +		**18**
	Second	1 +	**19**
First	4 −		**23**
	Second	7 =	**16**
First	+ 4 =		**20**
	Second	+ 1 =	**21**

You can play any of these games with variations on the keys pushed and the target numbers. Each involves different strategy, different perceptions.

Solitaire

The idea of the game is to use a solitary number, say 7, and to use only that number and the $+$, $-$, $\times$, $\div$ and $=$ keys, to see if you can get to the target number.

If your working number is 7, how can you get to 53? And if you can get to the target number, are there any ways to get there using fewer keys?

For example: If you want to get to 9, and your solitaire number is 2, you could do it this way:

$$2 \div 2 =$$
$$+ 2 +$$
$$2 +$$
$$2 +$$
$$2 =$$

But that's a total of 13 key strokes! A shorter way gives you the number 9 with only ten key strokes. The solution is in the back of the book if you need help.

Solitaire puzzles

Using only the keys 5, $+$, $-$, $\times$, $\div$ and $=$, can you get to .

126 in only 8 keystrokes? (You can use your constant or not—it doesn't count as a keystroke.)

Using only the keys 8, +, −, ×, ÷ and =, (with or without your constant), can you get to 89 in only 14 keystrokes?

For this one, you may use only the number 13—that is, the keys 1 and 3 always have to be pushed in the correct order, and cannot be repeated without a function sign, as in 131 for example. Using only 1, 3, +, −, ×, ÷ and =, can you get to 11 in 13 keystrokes?

Birthday game

Have you ever wanted to be able to figure out somebody's birthday without asking him? Well, you can do it with your calculator.

Give him the calculator. Tell him to put in the number of the month he was born in—without showing it to you. For example, if he was born in June (the 6th month) he should enter 6. If he was born in December, key in 12.

Then ask him to follow these easy-to-remember directions:

(Example birthday, April 19)

Key in birth month	4
+ 5 =	9
× 5 =	45
− 8 =	37
× 4 =	148
+ 5 =	153
× 5 =	765
add birth date (+19)	784
− 365 =	419

Now look at the calculator, and it will show the person's month and date of birth. In our example, the first digit is the birth month (4 for April), followed by the two digits of the birth date.

PLAYFUL PECKIN'

Keyboard patterns

The keyboard is full of patterns if you just let your fingers travel the keys without doing much thinking.

Adding and subtracting patterned numbers picked almost at random often produces a patterned answer that is quite surprising. Here are a few ideas to stimulate your keyboard doodling.

Zigzag

Add the sets of shaded keys following the arrows.

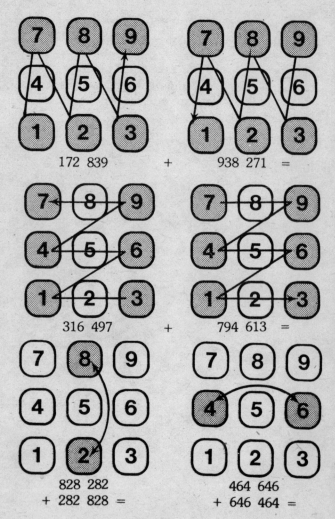

172 839 $+$ 938 271 $=$

316 497 $+$ 794 613 $=$

828 282 + 282 828 $=$

464 646 + 646 464 $=$

Up and back

Push the shaded keys in the order shown by the arrows.
Add the pair of numbers shown on each keyboard.

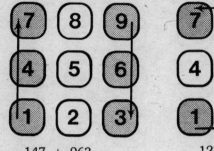

147 + 963 =

123 + 987 =

456 + 654 =

258 + 852 =

Topsy "T"

Subtract the smaller "T" pattern of shaded keys from the larger.

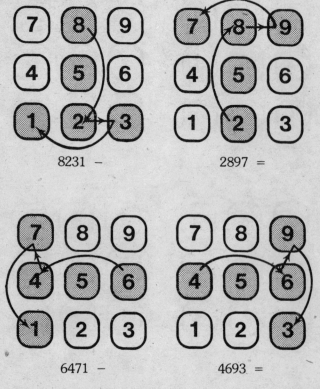

8231 −

2897 =

6471 −

4693 =

Multiply the second answer by 3 and compare it with the first answer.

Rebounding arrow

Subtract the smaller shaded "arrow" pattern from the larger, and write down your answer.

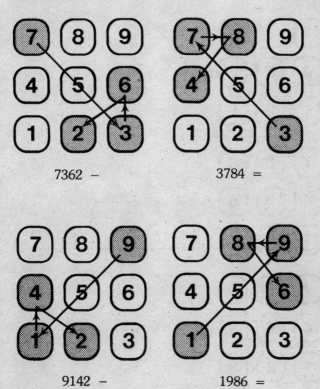

7362 −

3784 =

9142 −

1986 =

Multiply the first answer by two and compare it with the second answer.

PLAYFUL PECKIN'

To peck out these patterns, just go up the shaded keys, then push × and go down the same keys. Push = and write down your answer. Now, following the pattern at the right, subtract to find the differences in your answers. Subtract again to find the second differences, and you'll be in for a surprise.

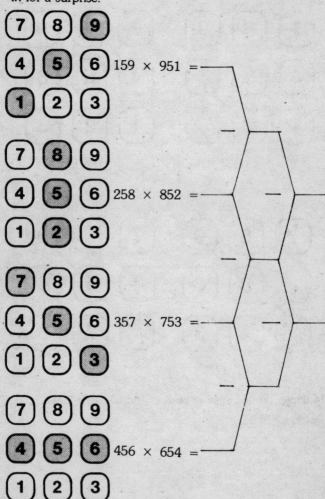

$159 \times 951 =$

$258 \times 852 =$

$357 \times 753 =$

$456 \times 654 =$

CREATURE FEATURES

When you're looking at somebody else's calculator—or even at your own—it's a good idea to know what to look for.

Here are some handy features you might look for in the next calculator you pick up:

ROUNDOFF
   If you do
   2 ÷ 3 =
   does the display read

$$0.6666667$$

If it does, then the calculator rounds off the last digit. If it reads 0 .666 666 6, then it doesn't round.

CONSTANT + AND −
   If you do
   5 + = = =
   does the display read:

$$10 \quad 15 \quad 20 \quad 25$$

If it does, the calculator has a constant for addition—a handy feature.

12-DIGIT ACCURACY

If you do:
111.111 11 × 111.111 11 =
the display will read:

1 2 3 4 5.6 7 8

But, if you subtract 123 45.6 you may get:

0.0 7 8 7 6 5 4

If you get the above—you know that the calculator stores more digits than it's showing. Very convenient for calculations with long numbers.

CLEAR OVERLOAD—If you pump in two big factors:

555 567 × 83 838 383 =
the display will read:

4 6 5 7 7 6 6.3 6

Notice the little circle or star or dot that appears on the display to tell you that the answer is too big to fit on the display. Now try adding 1 to the number. Push + 1 = . On most calculators, you don't get anything. Now push the key that says either CE or CL, and try adding 1 again. On some calculators, pushing the CE or CL button clears the overload and allows you to continue your calculations! It's especially nice when you're dealing with large figures.

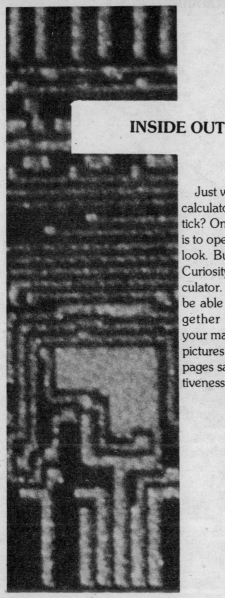

INSIDE OUT

Just what is inside your calculator? What makes it tick? One way to find out is to open it up and take a look. But be forewarned: Curiosity can kill the calculator. You may never be able to put it back together again. So save your machine, and let the pictures on the following pages satisfy your inquisitiveness.

THE BODY: a typical calculator.

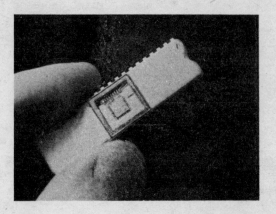

THE BRAIN: the tiny semiconductor chip in the center does all the figuring.

BLOW-UP: Resembling an aerial photo of a city, this enlargement of the 1/6'' chip shows it to be a busy nerve center indeed. The wires leading to and from the chip connect with broad, gold-plated conductors that carry the current to the "legs" of the chip. For still a closer look, turn the page. . . .

AMAZING MAZE: A section of the chip, magnified several hundred times, shows the complex arrangement of the transistor network. A single chip may contain up to 10,000 transistors. To make a circuit this tiny, a large blueprint is first drawn up to exacting standards. The drawing is then reduced photographically and finally "etched" into the crystalized, polished silicon chip.

Preparing for surgery:
The calculator pops open,

. . . revealing the entire circuit board. The upright section is the back of the keyboard. Notice the twelve flexible metal strips that connect the keyboard to the circuit board. At the top is the display window. The section containing the batteries has been removed so you can see more of the circuit board.

The clump of wire "legs" at left connects the display to the circuit board. Some of the wires are insulated and some are bare. To the right of the clump are two resistors bridging a stream of painted circuits. Electricity at a very low voltage passes through these "painted wires."

The "brain" is housed in black panel at top. The flat component just below panel is a bank of resistors. The three circular discs are capacitors, which store charges of electricity. The large can that looks like a fire extinguisher is also a capacitor.

Every piece is attached to the circuit board with wire "legs." One of the legs to this capacitor has been unsoldered and pulled out of the circuit board.

Let's see what's happening under the keyboard. . . .

The keyboard is removed and —oops! All the springs have fallen off their keys and ended up at the bottom of the keyboard. The printed circuit below the keyboard has contact dots that are split. The keys press down on the dots, carrying electricity from one side to the other and switching the current on.

White plastic keys are set in square holes in the keyboard cover. The center of each key is made of rubber.

Here, one of the key centers has been removed to show how it strikes the printed circuit board. The graphite base enables it to conduct electricity from one side to the other. A thin, plastic gasket keeps the springs from touching the printed circuits. The springs, of course, push the keys back up after they are pressed down.

The display is removed. It is made of glass and sealed air-tight, like a vacuum tube. Each segment inside the display lights up when current is applied. Short dashes form the various number patterns in each segment. Notice that when all the dashes in a pattern are visible, they appear as an 8.

The solder spots on the back of the circuit board show where the "legs" of each part are secured to the circuit board.

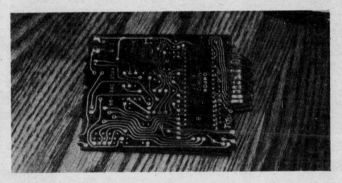

This is the top of the circuit board with almost all the components gone. The only things left are a round transformer and the black panel that houses the brain chip.

Could you put it back together again? Fortunately, you don't have to, but at least now you have an idea of what makes that calculator of yours so brainy.

CALENDAR PATTERNS

S	M	T	W	T	F	S
	1	2	3	4	5	6
7	8	9	10	11	12	13
14	15	16	17	18	19	20
21	22	23	24	25	26	27
28	29	30	31			

Crazy calendar

Use this month's calendar, or if you don't have one handy, use the one on this page.

Make a box around any nine dates, as we did. Ring the four dates in the corners.

	Our example	**Readout**
Multiply the dates in	$3 \times 19 =$	**5 7**
the opposite corners of	$5 \times 17 =$	**8 5**
the box together.		
Subtract the smaller answer from the larger.	$85 - 57 =$	**2 8**

What is your answer?
What did we get?
Try it using other dates.
See Solutions in the back for other clues.

Another calendar concoction

Use your own calendar or use the one on this page. Ring four numbers in a row—they have to be on the same line—as we did on the calendar to the right.

Multiply each number by the date below it:

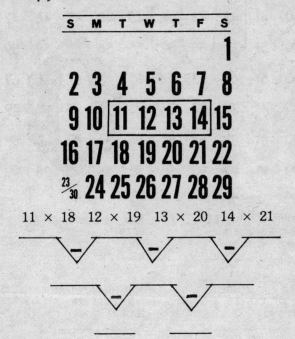

S	M	T	W	T	F	S
						1
2	3	4	5	6	7	8
9	10	11	12	13	14	15
16	17	18	19	20	21	22
23/30	24	25	26	27	28	29

11 × 18   12 × 19   13 × 20   14 × 21

Subtract each product from that of its neighbor. Write down the difference between them.

Subtract again. No matter what numbers you started with, you will always get 2!

THE RING

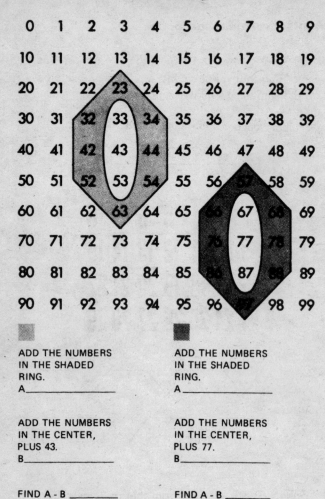

0	1	2	3	4	5	6	7	8	9
10	11	12	13	14	15	16	17	18	19
20	21	22	23	24	25	26	27	28	29
30	31	32	33	34	35	36	37	38	39
40	41	42	43	44	45	46	47	48	49
50	51	52	53	54	55	56	57	58	59
60	61	62	63	64	65	66	67	68	69
70	71	72	73	74	75	76	77	78	79
80	81	82	83	84	85	86	87	88	89
90	91	92	93	94	95	96	97	98	99

ADD THE NUMBERS
IN THE SHADED
RING.
A_____

ADD THE NUMBERS
IN THE SHADED
RING.
A_____

ADD THE NUMBERS
IN THE CENTER,
PLUS 43.
B_____

ADD THE NUMBERS
IN THE CENTER,
PLUS 77.
B_____

FIND A - B _____

FIND A - B _____

from PATTERNS TO PLAY ON A HUNDRED CHART by
Wallace Judd. © 1975, Creative Publications. Used with
permission.

PATTERN POCKET #1

In school (before the calculator) cranking out the long division in order to get a repeating decimal was so difficult that there wasn't much done with them.

But your calculator will give you repeating decimals with the flick of a finger, so here are a few that may interest you.

Put your constant on.

Try 5 ÷ 37 =

     7 =

     8 =

    11 =

    33 =

    34 =

Notice that groups of three digits in the decimal always add up to 9 or multiples of 9.

Does this always work for a repeating decimal?

Some other interesting divisors to try are 7, 101, and 99.

Try these—notice a pattern that you can use to make up your own.

$$37 \div 99 = \qquad 64 \div 99 =$$
$$48 \div 99 = \qquad 98 \div 99 =$$
$$81 \div 99 = \qquad 5 \div 99 =$$

$$606 \div 999 = \qquad 678 \div 999 =$$
$$543 \div 999 = \qquad 508 \div 999 =$$
$$712 \div 999 = \qquad 639 \div 999 =$$
$$234 \div 999 = \qquad 246 \div 999 =$$

$$2345 \div 9999 = \qquad 8765 \div 9999 =$$
$$1234 \div 9999 = \qquad 5636 \div 9999 =$$

To make up repeating decimals from numbers less obvious than multiples of 9, divide both the repeating number and the nines multiple by another number. For example, to make up a repeater that will result in 504, you could use $504 \div 999$. But the result is less obvious if you divide both numbers by, say, 36. $504 \div 36 = 14$ and $999 \div 36 = 27.75$. So $14 \div 27.75 = 0.504 \ 504 \ 5$.

Table talk

Pick any number in the table. Ring it.

(The example to the right is ours. You pick another number.)

36	120	(48)	24
15	50	20	10
3	10	4	2
18	60	24	12

Now cross out all the other numbers in the same row and column as the number you picked.

36	120	(48)	24
15	50	20	10
3	10	4	2
18	60	24	12

Pick any other number that is not crossed out. Ring it—then cross out all the other numbers in its row and column.

36	120	(48)	24
(15)	50	20	10
3	10	4	2
18	60	24	12

Pick a third number that is not ringed or crossed out. Ring it, and cross out every other number in its row and column.

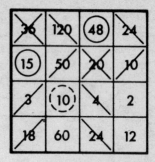

There should be one number left. Ring it.

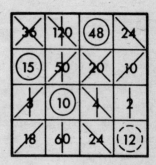

Now, multiply the four numbers you ringed.

With our 48 × 15 × 10 × 12 =

we got **86400**

What did you get?

EXPANDING CROSS

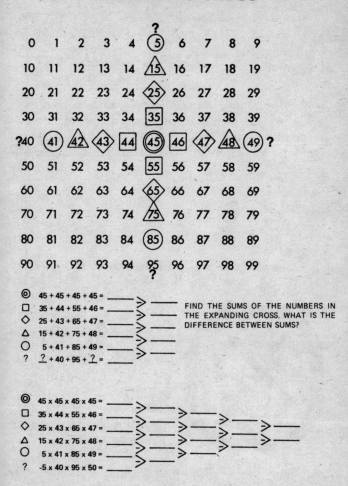

```
                       ?
   0   1   2   3   4  (5)  6   7   8   9

  10  11  12  13  14 /15\ 16  17  18  19

  20  21  22  23  24 <25> 26  27  28  29

  30  31  32  33  34 [35] 36  37  38  39

?40 (41)/42\<43>[44](45)[46]<47>/48\(49) ?

  50  51  52  53  54 [55] 56  57  58  59

  60  61  62  63  64 <65> 66  67  68  69

  70  71  72  73  74 \75/ 76  77  78  79

  80  81  82  83  84 (85) 86  87  88  89

  90  91  92  93  94  95  96  97  98  99
                       ?
```

◎ 45 + 45 + 45 + 45 = _____ ⟩ _____
□ 35 + 44 + 55 + 46 = _____ ⟩ _____   FIND THE SUMS OF THE NUMBERS IN
◇ 25 + 43 + 65 + 47 = _____ ⟩ _____   THE EXPANDING CROSS. WHAT IS THE
△ 15 + 42 + 75 + 48 = _____ ⟩ _____   DIFFERENCE BETWEEN SUMS?
○   5 + 41 + 85 + 49 = _____ ⟩ _____
? _?_ + 40 + 95 + _?_ = _____ ⟩ _____

◎ 45 x 45 x 45 x 45 = _____ ⟩ _____ ⟩ _____ ⟩ _____
□ 35 x 44 x 55 x 46 = _____ ⟩ _____ ⟩ _____ ⟩ _____
◇ 25 x 43 x 65 x 47 = _____ ⟩ _____ ⟩ _____ ⟩ _____
△ 15 x 42 x 75 x 48 = _____ ⟩ _____ ⟩ _____ ⟩ _____
○   5 x 41 x 85 x 49 = _____ ⟩ _____ ⟩ _____
? -5 x 40 x 95 x 50 = _____ ⟩ _____

from PATTERNS TO PLAY ON A HUNDRED CHART by
Wallace Judd. © 1975 by Creative Publications. Used
with permission.

STRETCHING YOUR CALCULATOR

Many expensive calculators have function keys that aren't on a mini-calculator. But there are easy ways for you to do the same operations that the additional keys perform—without having to pay extra for a "slide rule" calculator.

Reciprocal key

This key is for inversion. It gives you the reciprocal of whatever is on your readout.

If you have 5 on the readout, and push the key that says 1/x, it will give you 1/5, or 0.2. The simple way to do that on your calculator is to make sure it's on constant, then push ÷ = = . Try it—put 5 on your readout, then push ÷ = = . You get 0.2. It will work with any number on the display.

Power key

This key gives you x to the y power. If you want 2 to the 7th power, you can do it on a mini-calculator simply by putting 2 on the calculator, then (with your constant on) pushing $\times = = = = = =$. Notice that you push the $=$ key one less time than the power you want. This works for any positive, whole-number power. For a negative power, just push the division key instead of the multiplication key, and push the equal key one more time.

Pi key

The pi key simply lets you use the value of pi quickly in a calculation. The value of pi, to 7 decimal places, is 3.1415927. If you divide 355 by 113 on your calculator, you get the value 3.141 592 9—just 2 *ten-millionths* off. So, if you want to multiply a number by pi, just multiply by 355 and divide by 113.

Percent key

The percent key appears on many small calculators, though it can be easily replaced with a little thought. To find 37% of 155.27, just multiply .37 × 155.27 = . If you need to find the total of 6% tax added onto the total cost of $35.79, simply multiply 35.79 × 1.06 = . Your answer is 37.9374, or roughly $37.94.

To find what percent 45.37 is of 118.75, just do 45.37 ÷ 118.75 = and move the decimal place in the answer over two places to the right.

Square root without the key

The square root key is convenient in many situations, and if you have frequent need for it, it's worth getting a calculator with one. But if you're only going to find an occasional square root, here's a process that will help you.

The basic procedure is to make a guess, then divide the number you want to take the root of by that guess. Average your answer and the guess, and the result is your second guess. Divide the second guess into the root number, and average the result and the second guess. Keep doing this until your last guess and your next guess are nearly the same.

For example, to find the square root of 133:

Process	Key in	Readout
Divide 133 by 1st guess	133 ÷ 11 =	12.090 909
Average result & 1st guess	12.090 909 + 11 ÷ 2 =	11.545 454
Divide 133 by trial root	133 ÷ 11.545 454 =	11.519 685
Average result & trial root	11.519 685	
	+ 11.545 454 ÷ 2 =	11.532 569
Answer is your 3rd result.		
To check, square it.	11.532 569 × =	133.000 14

Notice that the result is only 14 hundred-thousandths away from the correct answer. If the first guess is at all close, three or four tries should get you very close to the square root of any number.

Using constant in square root

Your constant function can save a lot of time in finding the square root. Here are exactly the same steps as on the previous page, but done with a constant.

Key in	Readout	Purpose of keystrokes
133 ÷ 11 =	12.090 909	Divide first guess
+ 11 ÷ 2 =	11.545 454	Average result and 1st guess
÷ = = × 133 =	11.519 675	Divide 133 by trial root
+ 11.545 454 ÷ 2 =	11.532 564	Average result and trial root
÷ = = × 133 =	11.532 549	Divide 133 by trial root
+ 11.532 569 ÷ 2 =	11.532 559	Average result and trial root
× =	132.99 991	Check

Notice that for the first four steps, the readout is nearly the same as on the previous page. The answer was just taken one step further. The final step is a check to see how close to the square root the process has taken us. The answer is only nine hundred-thousandths off! You can see that by using the constant you save keying in all the extra numbers.

CONSUMER'S CORNER

This radial tire is guaranteed for 40 000 miles of use. The outside diameter of the tire is two feet two inches. How many times will the tire go around before the guarantee runs outs?

STEEL BELTED RADIAL

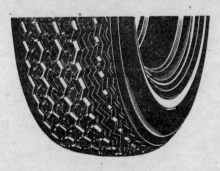

The John Hancock Towers, built in Boston, have been having trouble with windows falling out under high wind conditions. So they decided to replace all 10 344 windows in the building at a cost of $6 million.

How much did it cost them to replace each window?

Saving Gas

a. The average American drives about 14 000 miles a year—6000 in the city and 8000 on the highway.

1975 E.P.A. Gas Mileage Test Results

	City	Highway
Olds 98 400/V8	11	15
Nova Six	16	21
VW Rabbit	24	38

How much gasoline would be saved if 25 000 drivers switched from cars like the Olds 98 to a Nova Six? How much gasoline would be saved if they all switched from the Olds to a Rabbit?

b. An administration energy goal is to cut oil imports by a million barrels a day. One barrel of oil produces 13 gallons of gasoline. How many people would have to switch from cars that average 14 miles per gallon to cars that average 20 miles per gallon to meet the administration's goal?

WHAT'S WRONG?

Sometimes even calculators make mistakes. But at least they are consistent.

Here are the results from a calculator that was brought into Mr. Costain's fixit shop with one of the keys not working. Which key isn't working?

$$41.7 + 5079 = 5120.7$$

$$
\begin{array}{r}
131 \\
267 \\
538 \\
934 \\
+\ 728 \\
\hline
2358
\end{array}
$$

$$
\begin{array}{r}
82.6 \\
\times\ 85.91 \\
\hline
7044.62
\end{array}
$$

$$
\begin{array}{r}
307 \\
\times\ 68 \\
\hline
122
\end{array}
$$

WHAT'S WRONG?

Here is the record of a page from Angelina's checkbook. She assumed that her calculator was accurate. Unfortunately, she is overdrawn. What's wrong with her calculator? (Assume that she keyed in each number correctly and pushed the proper function key. What consistent error in her calculator could have resulted in these computations?)

CHECK NO.	DATE	TAX INFO	CHECK ISSUED TO	AMOUNT OF CHECK		IF SPEC CHG A/C LESS CHECK CHARGE		AMOUNT OF DEPOSIT		BALANCE	
										11 46	07
235	4/11	✓	Belly up Stock Co.	218	64					927	43
236	4/12	✓	Investment Division Service	513	37					611	86
	4/14		Pay day!					344	21	1156	07
237	4/17		Saudi Gas + Electric	99	42					1056	65
238	4/21	✓	Mr. Scrooge Bank	623	58					431	27
239	4/22		Brotherhood Food Stores	141	25					290	04

63

Giving a lecture at Segundo State, Mr. Sandy Nimblenumber was whipping along, calling out the numbers that appeared on his calculator display as he and the class worked through another assignment. Unfortunately, the students didn't follow along with their calculators, and you can see the nonsensical result of using his numbers.

What was wrong with Mr. Nimblenumber's calculator?

$384 \times 416 = 1414.4$

$187. + 4389 = 45.6$

$2196 \div 51.8 = 43.058\ 823$

$869 - 527 = 526.31$

$3084 \div 56 = .5428\ 571$

WHAT'S WRONG?

When Sue Thompson woke up to do her homework, she was sleepy and paid little attention to the numbers she put down for her answers.

When she had turned in her paper, the teacher gazed in wonderment at the fact that every answer was wrong! Then a smile spread over the teacher's face as she realized why everything was wrong.

Can you figure out what was wrong with Sue's calculator?

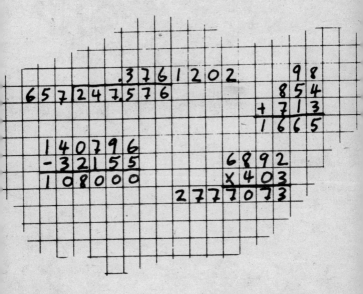

PERTINENT PROBLEMS

Beefalo steak

A steer converts grain into meat at the rate of about seven pounds of grain for one pound of meat.

Recently, however, a farmer in Stockton, California, developed a cross between a buffalo and a cow, sometimes called a beefalo. The beefalo tastes similar to steak, is juicy and tender. The advantage it has over a steer is that it can convert four pounds of grain into a pound of meat.

If you eat an average .32 pounds of beef a day, how much grain would be saved in a year if you ate beefalo instead of beef?

Tucker Trucker

Tucker Trucker drives a big rig all up and down Route 5, hustlin' loads and dodging chicken coops.

His rig usually rolls a little overweight—tonight he's loading 88 000 pounds. How much weight is on each of his eighteen wheels?

How much weight is on each wheel of your car? (If you don't know, assume your car weighs about 3500 pounds.)

Photography

Reconnaissance photography has advanced to such a state that a plane flying at 85 000 feet can take a picture so detailed that it will show a 10-foot-wide truck on a highway below.

Suppose a photographer wanted to use the same camera to take your picture. If he wanted to get detail down to individual hairs (about four thousandths of an inch wide), how far away from the camera would you have to sit?

Cementfog

The other day Cementfog Hairspray Company received an order from one of their wholesalers. The order read:

Purchase Order!
_____

FOR IMMEDIATE DELIVERY

42 432 832 cans of Cementfog Hairspray

Terms: 30 days after billing

--- --- --- --- --- --- --- ---

Unfortunately, the wholesalers couldn't be reached by phone to clarify their order. But the people at Cementfog Hairspray were sure the wholesalers knew the spray comes in boxes, with 36 cans in each box.

How many boxes of hairspray had they ordered?

Racer

A good race horse can run a mile in about 1 minute and 35 seconds. If a man who can run the 880-yard run in 2 minutes and 5 seconds was given a 1000-yard head start, who would win? And by how many yards?

(There are 5280 feet in a mile.)

Chain mail

Chain letters that request money are illegal. There were many chain letters around during their heyday in the 1930's. Suppose you got the following chain letter:

Dear Sucker,
Please put your name at the bottom of the sucker list and send a dime to the person at the top of the list. Cross off the top name and send copies of this letter to six rich friends, and if nobody breaks the chain, you, too, will be rich.

Sincerely,
Larson E. Whipsnade

E. Z. Money, Box 127, Grand Rapids, Mich.
A. L. Smith, Moorepark Expressway, San Jose, Ca.
Thrifty Goldgrubber, Boxtop Basin, N.M.
Samantha Snead, Chipanputt, New Jersey
Hard Lee Talkin, Cold Harbor, Me.
Jack Penny, Box 392, Pennypincher, Iowa
Clarabell Cloverleaf, Box 888, Los Angeles, Ca.

If no one broke the chain, how much money would you get back for your investment of a dime?

MAYBE YOU'D RATHER *NOT* KNOW

If you bought $15,000 worth of notes from the Cashbuilder Corporation when they were first offered, and held them until maturity, how much money do you stand to lose if the inflation rate holds steady at 11.7%?

NEW ISSUE   February 15, 1974

$400,000,000

Cashbuilder Corporation

7.60% Notes Due July 4, 1981

Price 100%
plus accrued interest from February 1, 1974

The Cashbuilder Corporation

Inflation

For the period ending January 31, 1975, the Consumer Price Index rose 11.7% over the previous year.

At that rate, what would a 59¢ loaf of bread cost in 25 years? (It should take about a minute to figure on your calculator.)

If the same rate of inflation (11.7%) keeps up, how much would a $53 000 house cost in 25 years?

And in 20 years, how much will it cost to send a student through college? (Assume that the current cost is about $20 000 for four years at a private college.)

Other increases

a. How much will the population of the U.S. increase if it were to increase only by 2.5% per year from 1975 to the year 2000? The 1975 population is about 213 million.

b. In the past 5 years, the national debt has grown on an average of 23%. In 1975 it stands at 500 billion dollars. At that average rate of increase, what will the national debt be in the year 2000?

c. Referring to answer a. (the number of people in the U.S. by the year 2000), how much will every man, woman, and child owe for the national debt by 2000?

COUNTERFEIT COWBOY AND COMPANY

At a Reno gambling casino one gambler was using counterfeit silver dollars. As long as he was throwing his money into the pot where it got mixed up with everyone else's, he would use only counterfeit coins. But whenever the coins were kept separate he always managed to use legal silver dollars.

Kate, who was a pretty sharp dealer herself, decided she'd find out who this counterfeit cowboy was. So she told all nine of the gents around the table to ante up by throwing their coins in the pot.

"Mix 'em up, boys," she said. "First one round the table antes up a dollar, second cowboy puts in two silver dollars, and so on 'round the table."

Since all the coins were getting put in the pot together, the counterfeit cowboy threw in all counterfeit coins, as Kate thought he would.

She grabbed the pot and walked over to the scale kept behind the bar for weighing nuggets. The coins weighed only 18 391.5 grains.

A true silver dollar should weigh 412.5 grains, but the counterfeit only weighed 384 grains. Who was the counterfeit cowboy?

Energy crisis ? ? ?

A number of companies currently are under investigation for falsely stating where they got their oil during the 1974 energy crisis.

The March 16 *The San Francisco Chronicle* reported:

During 1973, Coastal States (an oil firm) was Los Angeles' second largest supplier, selling the city 3.7 million barrels of fuel it identified as Venezuelan at prices ranging from $7 to $17 (per barrel).

Then, at the peak of the shortage in 1974, the city bought two Coastal States cargoes represented as having originated at Italian refineries. One 600,000-barrel cargo went for $24.23 a barrel and the other, 200,000 barrels, for $23.08.

If the oil was actually from Venezuela and should have sold for $12 a barrel (the average price the year before), how much profit did the company stand to make by misstating the country of origin for the oil?

The Seagram's 7 Crown label looks very much the same as it did last year—except for the fact that it says 80 proof instead of the 86 proof it was last year.

The bottle cost $5.59, and there were 7.2 million cases (at 12 bottles per case) sold last year.

Federal taxes on an 86-proof whiskey are $1.81, whereas the taxes on an 80-proof whiskey are only $1.68.

How much did the distiller save *in taxes alone* by reducing the alcoholic content of 7 Crown?

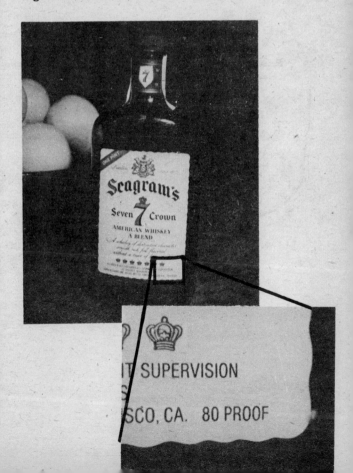

PATTERN POCKET #2

What happens when . . .
$$6 \times 7 =$$
$$66 \times 67 =$$
$$666 \times 667 =$$
$$6666 \times 6667 =$$
$$66666 \times 66667 =$$

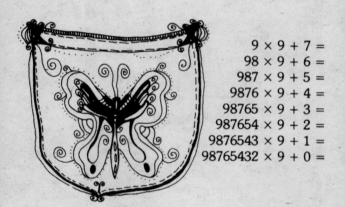

$$9 \times 9 + 7 =$$
$$98 \times 9 + 6 =$$
$$987 \times 9 + 5 =$$
$$9876 \times 9 + 4 =$$
$$98765 \times 9 + 3 =$$
$$987654 \times 9 + 2 =$$
$$9876543 \times 9 + 1 =$$
$$98765432 \times 9 + 0 =$$

Use your constant to do these multiplications, and they'll take you only a minute. See if you can find several patterns.

$7 \times 15873 =$
$14 \times 15873 =$
$54 \times 15873 =$
$45 \times 15873 =$
$28 \times 15873 =$
$63 \times 15873 =$
$62 \times 15873 =$
$26 \times 15873 =$
$15 \times 15873 =$
$51 \times 15873 =$

$39 \times 76923 =$
$78 \times 76923 =$
$52 \times 76923 =$
$117 \times 76923 =$
$104 \times 76923 =$
$26 \times 76923 =$

MAGIC SQUARES

Magic squares are supposed to have the same total for each row and for each column. In addition—they have the same sum for the sum of their diagonals.

This magic square is a little mixed up. One of its numbers is wrong. With your calculator it shouldn't take more than a minute to fix.

231	308	70
42	203	371
336	98	175

Here's another magic square—a good bit bigger than the other one. Every row, every column, and every diagonal is supposed to add up to the same number.

Again, just one of the numbers was miscalculated—and I'm sure that in a minute or two you can figure out which one.

175	91	182	133	224
112	63	154	105	196
84	210	126	217	168
56	147	98	198	140
203	119	70	161	78

BELIEVE IT OR NOT . . .

Expansion joints in the Golden Gate Bridge

On a warm day, the Golden Gate Bridge, which is about a mile long, expands almost two feet. Fortunately, expansion joints take up the extra length.

But if there were no expansion joints, how big a hump would the extra length cause in the bridge?

Another kind of expansion

If you loosen your belt by two notches, presumably a certain amount of space develops between your body and your belt—as shown in the diagram.

Assume that your waist is a circle with a diameter of 7.7 inches (about a 24'' waist). If you let your belt out 2 notches—call it 2 inches—how much space would be added between you and your belt?

Now assume that a very rotund person with a diameter through the waist of 16 inches let his or her belt out 2 inches. How much space would be added between his or her belt and body?

HOW DO YOU DO . . . ?

a. How do you add up the grocery list and figure the tax
    without writing down the total?

$$4.39$$
$$5.79$$
$$1.44$$
$$.69$$
$$+ \ 6\% \ \text{tax} \ =$$

b. Can you get your calculator to do this problem? (You
    can write down part of your answer.)

$$234 \ 567 \ 891$$
$$\times \ \underline{123 \ 456 \ 789}$$

c. Okay, smarty pants, can you get your calculator to do this long division?

$$13 \overline{)\ 100\ 000\ 000\ 000\ 000\ 000\ 000.}$$

(Here, you don't need to write anything down)

d. Your company ordered 144 widgets at $29.33 and also got 177 wobblecranks at $84.95. Can you figure out how much the total cost was, *without* using your memory or a piece of paper to recall the total cost of one of the items?

e. Can you do these on your calculator without writing anything down?

$$\frac{1 \times 3 \times 5 \times 7 \times 9 \times 11 \times 13 \times 15 \times 17 \times 19 \times 21}{2 \times 4 \times 6 \times 8 \times 10 \times 12 \times 14 \times 16 \times 18 \times 20 \times 22}$$

If you get an answer, is yours the most accurate answer you can get on your calculator?

f. Here's another that's a little easier to put on your calculator—but just as hard to figure out. What is the most accurate way to compute the value of this fraction—wholly on your calculator?

$$\frac{2847 \times 38945 \times 6789}{885588 \times 23456}$$

Ways and means

When adding two fractions it isn't necessary to compute the decimal value of one, then write it down and key it in again when you've figured out what the other fraction is.

On a mini-calculator you *can* add $\frac{113}{57} + \frac{41}{7}$ without memory and without writing down the decimal values of one of the terms. How?

Two boys were choosing up sides for their basketball teams from among the eight other boys standing against the fence.

Can you figure out what the odds were that they would pick a boy on the end of the line (on either end of it) down until the last person was picked? (No fair writing down a partial answer and feeding it into your calculator later.)

The Ultimate Problem

If you can do this one on your calculator—you have arrived. All of the work up to now in this section has been preparation for this little question.

Sirens cost $56.87 apiece, and flashing light sets cost $285.94. The Metropolis police force has 895 cruisers, and the fire department has 715 pieces of emergency equipment.

How much would it cost to equip all the cruisers and emergency vehicles with sirens and new light sets?

Can you do the entire problem on your calculator, without pencil and paper? The problem is extremely easy if you just add the costs together and add the vehicles, then multiply. But it's a real challenge to see if you can do it entirely on your calculator.

HOW TO. . . . . .

Work with minutes and seconds

Sometimes you need to do computations with minutes and seconds—and you don't want to convert entirely to seconds (or minutes).

To do the computations on your mini-calculator, keeping the units separate, you can use several zeros between the minutes and seconds to isolate them.

For example, to do
     27 minutes 41 seconds,
  + 18 minutes 33 seconds

Key in	Readout
27 000 41	*27 0 0 0 4 1*
+ 18 000 33 =	*45 0 0 0 7 4*

Notice that you can read your answer in minutes and seconds. You have to reduce the number of seconds over one minute in a separate operation.

This process is convenient to use with any of the English units like feet and inches, quarts and pints, or pounds and ounces.

Find the principal

At tax time, you can deduct the interest expense payments made on your house, land, or car from your gross income. Usually, the bank sends you a statement that tells how much interest you paid back and how much principal. But sometimes you'd like to be able to check this statement—or you may have lost the statement and have to do your own computing. Here's how:

You're paying off a $48 000 mortgage at 11.3% interest in monthly payments of $515. How much principal will you be paying in the 17th payment?

Readout

Step   1. 515 × 12 ÷ .113

           − 48 000 = 5590.265

     2. ÷ 12 × .113 =

        (Write down) 52.999995

Clear 3. .113 ÷ 12 + 1 = 1.0094166
All

     4. × = = = = = =

= = = = = = = = = = = 1.1617878

        (15 = pushes)

     5. × 62.999 995 (from

           step 2) = 73.192525

The principal that you'll be paying with the seventeenth payment is $73.19. Not much, is it?

Just going over the process—this is how it is done:

Step 1. Monthly payment times 12, divided by the interest rate, minus the amount of the loan.

Step 2. Continue dividing by 12, then multiplying by the interest rate. *Write down your result.*

Step 3. Clear the calculator. Input the interest rate, divide by 12, add 1 equals.

Step 4. Continue with the calculator on CONSTANT. Push the × key, then push the equals key *two less times* than the number of the payment you're interested in.

Step 5. Continue by multiplying by the result from step 2. Your answer is the amount of principal paid on that payment.

To find the amount of interest, just subtract the principal from the total payment. In our example from the previous page, the amount of interest on the 17th payment would be $441.81.

Pick a random number

There are computer programs that will generate random numbers—but you can generate them on the calculator easily enough. Here's how:

Pick the position in the readout where you want your random digit to appear. Let's say you pick the second digit in the display. So whatever number appears in the readout as the *second* digit at the end of the process is the number you'll use.

Now, input a single digit, decimal point, and at least four more digits.

Then push × and =, × and =, until the machine overloads. The digit that is second in the display when it overloads is your random digit.

Example   **Readout**
4.5386 × = × = ×
        = × = 324.15315

Your random number happens to be 2 in this case.

Are You Psychic?

Do you think you have psychic powers? Would you like to find out? Here's a simple method that you can use with your calculator.

First, think of a digit from 0 to 9, and predict where it will show on the calculator. For example, a prediction might be, "The digit 4 will be the third digit from the left on the readout."

Then generate a random number, following the directions on the previous page.

Repeat the process *ten* times, keeping track of the number of correct "predictions" you make.

To find out how psychic you are, turn the page. . . .

Use the chart below to see how psychic you are.

Number of Correct Guesses	Odds That You'd Get That Many Right	Psi Level
0	about 1 out of 3	washout
1	almost 4 in 10	straight
2	about 1 in 5	dreamer
3	better than 1 in 20	neighborhood seer
4	about 1 in 100	astrologer
5	better than 1 in 1000	minor prophet
6	about 1 in 10 000	major prophet
7	about 1 in 100 000	soothsayer
8	about 3 in ten million	interplanetary visitor
9	9 in a billion	seer or seeress
10	1 in 10 billion	psychic—call Duke University

Seriously, if you consistently predict more than five out of ten correctly, write the Institute for Parapsychology, Box 6847, College Station, Durham, North Carolina, 27708. They collect instances of psychic phenomena, and may be interested in your powers.

For more information on "psychic-power" probability, refer to this page in the solutions section.

PATTERN POCKET #3

Put your calculator on constant, then have fun banging away at these patterns. (If you use your constant, the whole set should take about a minute.)

$36 \times 987.654\,32 =$
$9 \times 987.654\,32 =$

$81 \times 987.654\,32 =$
$64 \times 987.654\,32 =$

$63 \times 987.654\,32 =$
$54 \times 987.654\,32 =$
$99 \times 987.654\,32 =$

$6 \times 987.654\,32 =$
$8 \times 987.654\,32 =$
$13 \times 987.654\,32 =$
$12 \times 987.654\,32 =$

Hidden digits

In each of the patterns on these pages, there are digits that appear in the middle.

See if you can make up some patterns that have a "hidden digit".

3 × 5 =	55 × 33 =
33 × 5 =	555 × 33 =
333 × 5 =	5555 × 33 =
3333 × 5 =	55 555 × 33 =
33 333 × 5 =	555 555 × 33 =

78 × 77 =	8 × 6 =
78 × 777 =	68 × 6 =
78 × 7777 =	668 × 6 =
78 × 77 777 =	6668 × 6 =
78 × 7 777 777 =	66 668 × 6 =
78 × 7 777 777 =	666 668 × 6 =

$$9 \times 9 = \qquad 9 \times 89 =$$
$$99 \times 89 = \qquad 99 \times 889 =$$
$$999 \times 889 = \qquad 999 \times 8889 =$$
$$9\ 999 \times 8\ 889 = \qquad 9999 \times 88\ 889 =$$
$$99\ 999 \times 88\ 889 = \qquad 99\ 999 \times 888\ 889 =$$

$$6 \times 4 = \qquad 6 \times 7 =$$
$$6 \times 44 = \qquad 6 \times 77 =$$
$$6 \times 444 = \qquad 6 \times 777 =$$
$$6 \times 4444 = \qquad 6 \times 7777 =$$
$$6 \times 44\ 444 = \qquad 6 \times 77\ 777 =$$

An unusual one is:
$$6 \times 4 =$$
$$66 \times 64 =$$
$$666 \times 664 =$$
$$6666 \times 6664 =$$
$$66\ 666 \times 66\ 664 =$$

MEMORY MADNESS

If your calculator has a memory (or if you can lay your hands on one that does), you can find the limit of the series below very easily.

Just enter the fraction, then put it in memory, multiply the fraction by itself (with your constant), put that result in memory, and keep alternating the multiplication with storage.

The result you'll have stored when the fraction is extremely small approaches the limit of the sum of the series.

$$1/2 + (1/2)^2 + (1/2)^3 + (1/2)^4 + \ldots$$
$$1/3 + (1/3)^2 + (1/3)^3 + (1/3)^4 + \ldots$$
$$1/5 + (1/5)^2 + (1/5)^3 + (1/5)^4 + \ldots$$

You can try these with different denominators—and the limits the sums approach are just astounding.

Pull a Switch

Suppose you have one number in the memory of your calculator—say 484 848. And there is another number on the readout of your calculator—say 333 333.

How can you switch the number from the readout into memory and the number from memory onto the readout without having to write down or remember either of them?

The Problem

Readout	Memory

What you have is: **333333   484848**

What you want is: **484848   333333**

How do you make the switch entirely in your calculator, using only the function keys?

On a calculator with a memory, you can calculate an approximation to *e* in only eleven steps, in about 30 seconds. Try it.

$$e = 1 + \frac{1}{1!} + \frac{1}{2!} + \frac{1}{3!} + \quad \ldots$$

If you figure out how to do the next one without having to start from scratch at each term, you'll have no difficulty figuring out any of these converging series.

$$e^X = 1 + \frac{x^1}{1!} + \frac{x^2}{2!} + \frac{x^3}{3!} + \quad \ldots$$

Don't let their appearance frighten you—these series are harmless. Just remember that 4! means $4 \times 3 \times 2 \times 1$. Your calculator makes these *simple*. If you don't believe that, just turn to the solutions.

The Swami

Remember the old swami-and-the-chessboard-filled-with-grain problem? The one in which the swami does the raja a great favor, and the raja says, "What do you wish?" Then the swami says, "Only a slight favor—that you put one grain of wheat on the first square of my chessboard, two grains on the second square, four grains on the third, and so on, doubling each time until you have covered all the squares of the chessboard."

So the raja has his slave get a bag of grain and finds it slightly insufficient to fill all the 64 squares of the chessboard.

If you have a calculator with a memory, without writing anything down, can you figure out how many grains of wheat it took to fill the chessboard?

(It's not as easy as it looks.)

Don't worry about finding any but the first eight significant digits.

FAR OUT

If you really want some challenging problems that *can* be done on a small calculator—try a few of these.

$$\sqrt{2} = 1 + \cfrac{1}{2 + \cfrac{1}{2 + \cfrac{1}{2 + \cfrac{1}{2 + \ldots}}}}$$

Using this formula, compute the square root of two. When you think you've got it, check your answer by finding the square root of two with the method on pages 52-54.

When you've got that in hand, try to see whether the following is true.

$$\text{Does } \sqrt{3} = 1 + \cfrac{1}{3 + \cfrac{1}{3 + \cfrac{1}{3 + \cfrac{1}{3 + \ldots}}}}$$

Your calculator doesn't have to have a memory to be able to do these. Once you figure out how to put the problems on your calculator—a pattern will show up almost immediately.

$$(9984 \times 9984) - (9985 \times 9983) =$$
$$(9984 \times 9984) - (9986 \times 9982) =$$
$$(9984 \times 9984) - (9987 \times 9981) =$$

$$(17 \times 17) - (18 \times 16) =$$
$$(17 \times 17) - (19 \times 15) =$$
$$(17 \times 17) - (20 \times 14) =$$

$$(.4 \times .4) - (1.4 \times -.6) =$$
$$(.4 \times .4) - (2.4 \times -1.6) =$$
$$(.4 \times .4) - (3.4 \times -2.6) =$$

THE OUTER LIMITS

Go down each column, computing with bigger and bigger numbers replacing the number that changes. Notice what's happening. As the denominator gets bigger the readout gets closer to zero.

$1 \div 2 =$ $1 \div 1 =$

$1 \div 3 =$ $1 \div .1 =$

$1 \div 4 =$ $1 \div .05 =$

$1 \div 10 =$ $1 \div .02 =$

$1 \div 220 =$ $1 \div .002 =$

$1 \div 55555 =$ $1 \div .000\ 3 =$

$1 \div 666\ 666 =$ $1 \div .000\ 002 =$

$1 \div 7\ 777\ 777 =$ $1 \div .000\ 000\ 02 =$

$1 \div 88\ 888\ 888 =$ $1 \div .000\ 000\ 01 =$

$1 \div 99\ 999\ 999 =$

Go down each column, and as you do, notice what's happening to your answer.

.000 01 + 40 ÷ .000 01 =
.000 1 + 40 ÷ .001 =
.001 + 40 ÷ .001 =
.01 + 40 ÷ .01 =
.1 + 40 ÷ .1 =
.5 + 40 ÷ .5 =
.9 + 40 ÷ .9 =

1 + 40 ÷ 1 =
2 + 40 ÷ 2 =
22 + 40 ÷ 22 =
333 + 40 ÷ 333 =
4 444 + 40 ÷ 4 444 =
55 555 + 40 ÷ 55 555 =
666 666 + 40 ÷ 666 666 =
7 777 777 + 40 ÷ 7 777 777 =
88 888 888 + 40 ÷ 88 888 888 =

17 × 1 + 4 ÷ 1 =
17 × 5 + 4 ÷ 5 =
17 × 10 + 4 ÷ 10 =
17 × 22 + 4 ÷ 22 =
17 × 333 + 4 ÷ 333 =
17 × 55 555 + 4 ÷ 55 555 =
17 × 666 666 + 4 ÷ 666 666 =
17 × 99 999 999 + 4 ÷ 99 999 999 =

TYPES OF CALCULATORS

Mini

The basic four-function machine adds, subtracts, multiplies, and divides. Usually it has a constant, either built into it or as a switch. Some of the better models include a constant plus and minus, as well as the standard multiplication and division constant. Normally the readout is eight digits and there is automatic floating decimal placement, so the machine always reads out the eight most significant digits. The mini is the least expensive of the calculators and, with some of the tricks taught in the chapter "Stretching Your Calculator," can easily imitate many of the higher-priced models.

Memory

A memory leaves your calculator free to do calculations while a subtotal is stored away in the memory. In doing your taxes, for example, you can store the subtotal to, say, line 16 while you are computing 35% of line 17 to add to it. It can also provide running totals to two different columns at the same time, which is especially convenient if you have to turn pages to locate data. A memory usually adds about $15 or $20 to the cost of a calculator. You don't need to pay extra for the memory minus key, which subtracts the number in the readout from the memory total, since you can multiply the readout by minus one and add it to the memory.

Slide rule

A "slide rule" calculator is in many ways a misnomer. It is also an expensive calculator that can do little more than a mini. Every key on the slide rule calculator can be duplicated by one or two keystrokes on the mini—except for the square root key. The methods for copying the slide rule calculator with a mini are detailed in the chapter, "Stretching Your Calculator," beginning on page 50. The name "slide rule calculator" is a misnomer because a good, average slide rule has the trigonometric functions and logarithmic functions on it that the "slide rule" calculator doesn't have. Unless you have great need of a square root key, the "slide rule" calculator is no bargain at any price.

Scientific

This calculator might also be called the "mathematic" calculator, since mathematicians as well as scientists have great use for the functions included on it. The scientific calculator usually has all the trigonometric functions—sine, cosine, and tangent—as well as keys to find rational powers and roots of numbers. Sometimes this type of calculator comes without a memory, which is a shame, since most of the complex calculations done with these rather sophisticated functions require a memory. This calculator is a must for students taking advanced math in high school or college, as well as for engineers, architects, and statisticians.

Business

The Hewlett-Packard Company puts out the most complete line of business pocket calculators. Many of these calculators include special functions of particular interest to professionals in a specific field. Insurance and banking personnel can take advantage of keys that compute interest, annuity, and mortgage, as well as computing the number of days between any two dates in the century. Other models are specifically designed for the needs of architects, mathematicians, and engineers. Some of the most sophisticated of these calculators are programmable, and as such are actually pocket-sized computers. Before purchasing, it's best to analyze all the models offered, and get the keyboard that best suits your specific needs.

SOLUTIONS

Page 13   ELBE
              hESSE
              LOBO
              GIGGLE

Page 14:   BIG.BOOBS
              SOhIO
              IGLOO

Page 15:   hIS.GOOSE
              hI.SLOB

Page 16:   hE
              BOILS
              hIS
              ShOE
              S.O
              hIS
              SOLE
              IS
              LOOSE

Page 17: Adding 18 181 818 to 24 242 424 will switch its digits, too. It will also switch 3535. . . and 4646. . . and 5757. . . , in fact, it will switch any numbers of this form as long as their difference is two.

Page 19 : If you divide the number, say 38, by .99, you will also get 38.383838.

   The trick works because $73 \times 101 \times 137 = 1\ 010\ 101$. And when you multiply 1 010 101 times any two-digit number, it makes it repeat.

Page 20: To make your calculator count by 5's, just multiply 10 000 000 by 1.000 000 5. To make it count by any digit, just use that digit as the last one in the multiplier 1.000 000 x.

Page 21: To make the machine count backwards by 1's, just start with 10 000 000 or less—or keep on going with the numbers you've got. When the countdown gets to 10 000 004. . . 10 000 002. . .10 000 000, the next number will be 9 999 999, followed by 9 999 998. . .9 999 997. . .and so on down by *ones*.

Page 22: The winning strategy is to play first and pick 1. Then whatever the other person adds, you add enough to make 5. For example, if opponent adds 2, you add 2; if he adds 3, you add 1. Then, whatever he adds, you make sure the total after your turn is 9. The key numbers after that are 13, 17, and 21. Notice that the numbers are four apart: 1, 5, 9, 13, 17, 21. After you're on a critical number, just add enough to whatever the other person picks to total four more. It's easy.

A similar strategy wins going to 50 with keys from 1 to 6—except that the critical numbers are seven apart.

Page 23: The strategy in this game is similar but takes longer to explain than to play—so, just enjoy the game. Hope you win.

Page 24: There are always ways to get any number by brute force. To get to 53 using only 7, you can do these keystrokes: $7 + 7 + 7 + 7 \div 7 = + 7 + 7 + 7 + 7 + 7 + 7 + 7 =$. It's rather tedious, but it does get one to 53 in 25 keystrokes. Notice that the first $=$ got you to the number 4, and from that you built by 7's to 53. A much shorter process is the following: $7 \times 7 \times 7 = + 7 + 7 + 7 + 7 \div 7$

= . The first = gets you to 49 × 7, or 343. If you divided now by 7, the answer would be 49. But you really want to get to 53—so each time you add 7 to 343, you're adding one to the answer you'll get when you divide the entire total by 7. 343 + 7 ÷ 7 is 50. 343 + 7 + 7 ÷ 7 gives 51, and so on.

To get to 9 using 2, do 2 × = = = + 2 ÷ 2 = .

Page 25: To get to 126 using 5 do:
5 × = = = + 5 = .
    To get to 89 using 8 do:
8 + 8 + 8 − 8 × = = = + 8 = .
    To get to 11 using 13 do:
− 13 − 13 − 13 + 13 = .

Page 28: These patterns work even when you do them backwards. If, for example, you begin the first one with 7182 . . . instead of 1728 . . . , the answer *still* comes out 1 111 110. And if in the second set, you mistakenly punch 134 679 + 976 431, the answer is again 1 111 110. In each exercise you push twelve digit-keys. If, instead, you pushed twelve 5's like this: 555 555 + 555 555, the answer is also 1 111 110.

Page 29: In all cases the answer is 1110.

Page 30: In both cases, your final answer for the process is 5334.

Page 31: The answer for both processes is 7156.

Page 32: Numbers	products	1st difference	2nd difference
159 × 951	151 209		
		68 607	
258 × 852	219 816		19 602
		49 005	
357 × 753	268 821		19 602
		29 403	
456 × 654	298 224		

Page 46: The difference will always be 28, no matter which nine dates you put the box around. The algebraic explanation is that the four corners can be represented by n, n + 2, n + 14, and n + 16. Multiplying opposite corners gives $n^2 + 16n$ for one product and $n^2 + 16n + 28$ for the other product. The second will always be 28 larger than the first product.

Page 47: We let the smallest date in the row be d. The process can be shown as:

	d	d+1	d+2	d+3
	d+7	d+8	d+9	d+10
Products are:	d^2+7d	d^2+9d+8	$d^2+11d+18$	$d^2+13d+30$
Differences are:	2d+8		2d+10	2d+12
2nd differences are:		2		2

The algebra shows that no matter what four dates in a row you pick, the second differences will always come out 2.

Page 48: You can make a transparent plastic hexagon to slide around over the hundred chart, and it would show the same relationships, no matter where you put it. For these rings:

	Sum Is	Center Total	A-B
First Ring:	344	172	172
Second Ring:	616	308	308

The sum of the outside numbers is always eight times the number in the exact center. The three middle numbers plus the exact center number are always four times the number in the exact center. So the difference is always four times the number in the exact center.

Page 49: The pattern doesn't always work—as you may have discovered when you divided a number by 99. For example, $800 \div 99 = 8.08080808$. The sum of the repeating groups is clearly not 9 or a multiple of 9.

Pages 51-52 The table was made up like this:

×	3	10	4	2
12	36	120	48	24
5	15	50	20	10
1	3	10	4	2
6	18	60	24	12

Notice that the product of the numbers used to make up the table is also 86 400. Every other product you generate by the process outlined on pages 47 and 48 will also be 86 400, since the process makes sure that each of the outside factors will contribute once and only once to the product.

Page 53: Expanding Cross—the sums are all 180. The numbers in the last line should be $-5 + 40 + 95 + 50$, and their sum is also 180.

Page 54: The inversion process works because your constant remembers the number that's on the readout if you don't put in another number between pressing the ÷ key and the − key. So if you press the keys $5 \div =$, the answer on your display is $5 \div 5$, or 1. Pressing the = key again divides again by 5, so the answer is $1 \div 5$ — the reciprocal of 5.

The x to the y power process works because your calculator remembers the number on the display if nothing else is keyed in between pressing the × and = keys.

Page 59: The tire has a diameter of 2 2/12 feet, or 2.166 666 feet, so when it rolls once, it goes pi times its diameter, or 6.806 784 4 feet. 40 000 miles is 211 200 000 feet. Dividing that entire distance by the distance the tire goes in one roll gives the number of times it rolls around—31 027 866 times! Assuming the tread wears about a half-inch in that time, how much does the tire wear in one mile?

Page 60: Six million dollars divided by 10 344 windows comes to a cost of $580.05 per window.

Unfortunately, windows cannot be replaced as fast as documents can be copied. If they could, builders would be able to install 10 802 windows an hour, or 180 a minute.

Page 61: a. If 25 000 drivers switched from Olds to Nova, the savings would be over 8 million gallons of gas in a year. If 25 000 drivers switched from Olds to Rabbits, the savings would be over 15 million gallons of gas per year. The figures are these:

GALLONS USED PER CAR

	City	Country	Total
Olds	545+	533+	1078+
Nova	375	381−	756−
Rabbit	250	210+	460+

The savings of the Nova over the Olds for one car is 322.8+ gallons, which means a savings of 8 070 887.5 gallons for 25 000 drivers. The Rabbit saves 618.2+ gallons over the Olds, which means a savings of 15 456 537 gallons for 25 000 drivers.

b. The average driver drives 38.8 miles each day, as you can figure out from the previous problem. At 14 mpg, it takes 2.7 gallons to drive that far, but at 20 mpg it only takes 1.94 gallons. The savings is .83 gallons per driver per day. 13 million gallons divided by the .83 saved by each economy-minded driver means that 15.6 million drivers would have to switch cars to save a million barrels of oil a day.

Page 62: The 6 key doesn't work. When Mr. Costain's customer pushes the key down, nothing happens.

Here is how to figure out what's wrong. First, see if any of the computations are exactly correct. If they are, it's most likely that the wrong key is not among those used in that computation. It's remotely possible that two keys are involved or that there are cancelling errors, but that's unlikely. On this page, $41.7 + 5079$ shows the correct answer. That means you can cross off 0, 1, 4, 5, 7, and 9 from the list of bad keys. The sum for the column addition is off by 60—it should be 2418 but it's 2358. In that case, the 3's could be reading as 1's and the sum would be 2358. Or the 6 could just not read. Dividing the product 1228 by its factors gives the decisive clue. $1228 \div 307 = 4$, so the 6 is not reading. This is verified by dividing the other product 7044.62 by 85.91.

Page 63: The first subtraction went fine, eliminating the keys 1, 2, 4, 6, and 8 from suspicion. The second subtraction is wrong. The balance should be 414.06, not 611.86. Subtracting the wrong answer from the previous balance, we note that 315.57 was subtracted, not the 513.37 that should have been. It looks as though the 3's and 5's were switched. The next addition confirms that observation, since 544.21 was added to the balance, not the 344.21 that was actually deposited. The 3 key is reading into the circuitry as a 5. Two checks later, the 3's and 5's are again interchanged, confirming the deduction that the 3 key reads as a 5 and the 5 key as a 3.

Page 64: Every computation gives the wrong answer, so there's no clue as to keys that do work. Dividing 1414.4 by 384 gives 3.6833333—no clue. But dividing 1414.4 by 416, its other factor, gives 3.4! It appears the 8 in 384 dropped out and was replaced by a decimal point. If the same thing happened in the next problem, instead of 187 going in, it would be 1.7 + 43.9. The sum is indeed 45.6, and we need look no further. The 8 key is read by the logic as a decimal point.

Page 65: The addition problem is correct, eliminating 1, 3, 4, 5, 7, 8, and 9 from consideration. But at the ones and tens place in the subtraction, 6, 5, and 9 all seem to be involved. If the 6 read as a 5, the last digit would be 0, but then what about the 90-50? Our first clue comes from the multiplication. 2 777 073 ÷ 403 is 6891, not 6892—the factor that was supposed to be there. The 2 was read as a 1. Multiplying the division answer, .3761202, by 657 gives 247.11097. Apparently the 5 and 7 were also read as 1's. Looking again at the subtraction shows that if the last three digits of each of the numbers were 1's, then the subtraction would come out as it appears. But what about the other, smaller numbers. If their "last three digits" were 1's, they would have been changed, too. In fact, in every number the first three digits were accepted as is. The logic changed every digit over the first three to a 1.

Page 66: If you eat .32 pounds of beef each day, that's 116.8 pounds of beef a year. A steer converts 7 pounds of grain to one pound of meat, so it has to eat 817.6 pounds of grain to be converted into meat. A beefalo converts 4 pounds of grain to a pound of meat, so it only has to eat 467.2 pounds of grain to make a pound of meat. The savings is 350.4 pounds of grain—about a pound of grain a day, or enough to feed one other person somewhere else in the world.

Page 68: 88 000 pounds on 18 wheels is 4888.8888 pounds on each wheel—more than the entire weight of your car on each one. The weight on each one of your tires is 3500 ÷ 4, or 875 pounds each.

Page 69: The truck is 120 inches wide. That is 30 000 times wider than the hair. So you could be 30 000 times closer to take the picture. 85 000 ÷ 30 000 is about 2.83 feet!

Page 70: The only digit that's unreadable is the hundreds digit. Substituting in 0, 1, 2, 3, . . . and so on for the hundreds digit, and dividing by the 36 cans in each box shows they must have ordered 42 432 732 cans of hairspray, or 1 178 687 boxes of the stuff.

Page 71: How far does the man run? He has a 1000-yard head start, so he only has to go 760 yards, since a mile is 1760 yards (or 5280 feet ÷ 3). How fast can the man run? He runs 880 yards in 125 seconds (2 minutes and 5 seconds), so he runs 7.04 yards each second. Dividing the 760 yards he has to run by the 7.04 yards he runs each second, shows that it will take him 107.9+ seconds to finish. That's a minute and 47.9+ seconds. Since the horse runs the mile in 1 minute and 35 seconds, he'll beat the man by 12.9+ seconds. Since the man runs 7.04 yards each second, he'll be 91 yards away from the finish line when the horse crosses it. (P.S., The world record for the 880 is 1:44.6. Who would win in that race?)

Page 72: If each person below you on the list had sent the letter to six friends who did likewise, you'd get 6 × 6 × 6 × 6 × 6 × 6 dimes, or 46 656 dimes, which is $4 665.60. Not bad for a dime investment—but unfortunately illegal.

Page 73: Since the inflation rate will vary substantially in the time from 1974 to 1981, the figures will not be worked out with fantastic detail. The maturity time is 7 years and 5 months. Interest at 7.6% on 15 000 dollars for 7 years is computed by these keystrokes: 15 000 × 1.076 = = = = = = =. At the end of 7 years the amount will be $25 048.23. Multiply this amount by 5/12 of 7.6% (or 3.16+ %), and you get a grand value of $25 841.43 for the Cashbuilder bonds. The amount of increase is $10 841.43—what looks to be a hefty return on a $15 000 investment.

But the purchasing power of the 15 000 dollars is shrinking at a rate of 11.7% per year. To see how many 1981 dollars it would take to be the equivalent of the 1974 dollars, compute 11.7% of 15 000 by following these keystrokes: 15 000 × 1.117 = = = = = = =. At the end of 7 years it would take $32 534.44 to equal the purchasing power of $15 000 in 1974. Add to that the additional 5 months' interest (4.875%), and you find the equivalent purchasing power over the whole period is $34 129.93. You have actually *lost* $8 288.50 (that is, $34 129.93 − 25 841.43) in purchasing power.

Page 74: Again, multiplying the cost of the bread by 1.117 gives the cost of the bread in one year at 11.7% increase. Multiplying with your constant shows that in 25 years a 59¢ loaf of bread will cost $9.38!

To find the additional percentage on a house, simply multiply the cost by 1.1117 as many times as you want to figure years of inflation. 53 000 × 1.117 = = = will give you three years' inflation cost. Pushing the = key 25 times will show the cost of the house to be $842 568.09 in 25 years!

The college costs will be 20 000 × 1.117 = = = . . ., pushing the = key 20 times. The answer is $182 849.31. One can hope that a student's increased earning power will make the investment worthwhile.

Page 75:

a. Convert the percentage gain into a number that automatically adds on the amount gained for the year. If your percent gain is 5, then multiply the figure by 1.05 to get the total at the end of the year. By keying 213×1.025 $= = = \ldots$, using the $=$ key as many times as you want to figure years, you get the total after so many years' increase. Pushing the $=$ key 25 times, you find that the U.S. population would be about 395 million in the year 2000.

b. The national debt growing at 23% every 5 years would give $500 \times 1.23 = = = = =$, or 1 407.6 billion dollars debt by the year 2000.

c. This would be $3564 for every person in the U.S. in 2000.

Page 76: The weight was 171 grains short. The pot contained 45 coins, and should have weighed 18 562.5 grains. Instead it weighed 18 391.5 grains. The counterfeit coins are 28.5 grains lighter than the real silver dollars, so there must have been six of them in the pot ($171 \div 28.5 = 6$). Since the first cowboy anted one coin, the second cowboy anted up two coins, and so on, the culprit must have been the sixth person around the table.

Page 78: The 600 000 barrels cargo was overpriced by $12.23 ($24.23 − 12.00$), so the profit on it would be $7 338 000. The 200 000 barrels cargo was overpriced by $11.08, so the excess profit on it would be $2 216 000. The total excess profits would be $9 554 000.

Page 79: The saving was $ .13 per bottle, so on the 12 bottles in a case, the distiller saved $1.56. Since in 1974 Seagram's 7 Crown sold 7.2 million cases, if they sell the same in 1975, they stand to save 7.2 times $1.56, or 11.232 million dollars.

Page 82: The number in the middle of the right-hand column should be 364 instead of 371. The sums of all rows, columns, and diagonals should be 609.

Page 83: The number in the bottom right-hand cell should be 77 rather than 78. The sum of all rows, columns, and diagonals should be 630.

Page 84: Imagine that the hump was exactly in the middle of the bridge.

1/2 mile + 1 foot   1/2 mile + 1 foot
                    hump
   1/2 mile   1/2 mile

The height of the hump can be seen to be the third side of a triangle. Since it's a right triangle, $a^2 + b^2 = c^2$. In this case $(hump)^2 + (2640)^2 = (2641)^2$. This means $(hump)^2 + 6\,969\,600 = 6\,974\,881$, or $(hump)^2 = 5281$. Now find the square root of 5281, and you'll discover that the hump would be *over 72 feet high!* (72.6705 feet, to be exact.)

This problem courtesy of Carole Greenes, professor of mathematics education, Boston University.

Page 85: Both the person with the 24″ waist and the fat person added a space of .3183+ inches between their body and their belt. (In fact, if you put a belt around the earth and let it out two inches, a space of .3183 inches would also develop between the earth and its belt!) 7.7 inches times pi gives a waist of 24.190 265 inches. Add 2 inches to that, and the distance around is 26.190 265. Divide by pi to find the radius, and you find it's now 8.336 608 9 inches, or .636 608 inches larger. Divide this by 2, since there's a space on both sides of the body, and you see the space added was .318 304 4 inches. (The same steps give the same answer for the earth or for the fat person.)

Page 86: a. Add up the column of figures and multiply by 1.06. In this case the subtotal is \$12.31. 12.31 × 1.06 = 13.0486, or \$13.05, for your total.

b. To do the long multiplication, simply multiply together each group of three digits as shown below. Make sure they're in the right place, and add. Zeroes merely indicate place holders when used this way 000 below.

```
                    234  567  891
              ×     123  456  789
                         702  999 . .891 × 789
                    447  363 . . . . . . . .567 000 × 789
               184  626 . . . . . . . . . . . . .234 000 000 × 789
                    406  296          891 × 456
               258  552               567 000 × 456
          106  704                    234 000 000 × 456
          109  593                    891 × 123
       69 741                         567 000 × 123
    28 782                            234 000 000 × 123
                              999     total them up by column
                         1361
                    2031
               1996
          957
    28
```

Carry any four-digit column
sums by adding to the digit in
front of it, and the total is 28 958 998 032 361 999.

Page 87: c. To begin with, 10 000 000 ÷ 13 = 769 230.76. What part of the answer are you sure is exactly right? You know that 769 230 is exact, so multiply it by 13. The answer is 9 999 990, just 10 off. Now 10 ÷ 13 gives the remainder—.769 230 7. Notice that .76 is a repeat of the last two digits of the previous answer. The answer so far is 7 692 307 692 307. To continue, repeat the process of chopping off the last two digits and multiply. You can divide any length of number by this process.

d. To make sure we get the right answer, let's just do it with a memory first. $(144 \times 29.33) + (177 \times 84.95)$ is the same as $4223.52 + 15\,036.15$, or $19\,259.67$. To do it without a memory, key: $177 \times 84.95 \div 144 + 29.33 \times 144 =$, and you'll get the answer, $19\,259.668$, which is about as close to the correct answer as you might wish. All done as neat as a whistle and without a memory.

For any of you curious about the algebra, it's $(a \times b) + (c \times d) = [\,(a \times b)/d + (c \times d)/d\,]\,d$, which cancels to $[\,(a \times b)/d + c\,]\,d$. The latter form is ready for your calculator.

Page 88: e. To do the problem on your calculator, you can simply alternate numerator and denominator, multiplying and dividing like this to get the answer: $1 \div 2 \times 3 \div 4 \times 5 \ldots$, continuing until you end with $\ldots \times 19 \div 20 \times 21 \div 22 =$. The answer to this process is $.168\,187\,7$. A more accurate answer is arrived at by multiplying factors in the numerator until the calculator almost overloads—then dividing by small numbers until there's room to do more multiplication. Do $1 \times 3 \times 5 \times \ldots \times 15 \times 17 \div 2 \div 4 \div 6 \div 8 \div 10 \times 19 \times 21 \div 12 \div 14 \ldots \div 20 \div 22 =$. The answer to this process is $.168\,188$.

An even more accurate process is to divide only multiples of 2, 4, and 5 in the first division, since these divisions result in terminating decimals. The process for this is: $1 \times 3 \times \ldots \times 15 \times 17 \div 2 \div 4 \div 8 \ldots \div 16 \times 19 \times 21 \div 20 \div 6 \div 12 \div 14 \div 18 \div 22 =$. The answer to this is $1.681\,880\,6$. Since the 10 was left out of the denominator, the answer is 10 times too big, and the real answer is $.168\,188\,06$! Quite accurate.

f. To do this problem, apply the principle of getting the biggest possible number in the numerator and dividing by the smallest possible number. This gives you

2847 × 6789 ÷ 23 456 × 38 945 ÷ 885 588 = 36.237 589. Doing it the obvious way with the first factor divided by the first denominator factor, etc., gives an answer of 36.236 966, more than 6 ten thousandths off.

Page 89: Key: 113 ÷ 57 × 7 + 41 ÷ 7 = . The answer is 7.839 598 8. The algebra is simply $a/b + c/d$, the same as $(ad/b + cd/d)/d$, or $(ad/b + c)/d$, which is ready to calculate on any mini.

The odds of choosing an "end" boy are always two out of how many are standing there. On the first choice, the odds are 2/8 of picking a person on the end of the row. On the second choice, the chances are 2/7 of picking an end person. With two people left standing, the odds are 2/2 of picking somebody on the end—there's no other choice! The odds of always picking "end" people, then, are 2/8 × 2/7 × 2/6 × 2/5 × 2/4 × 2/3 × 2/2 × 1/1. This is .003 174 6—not very good odds if the people are of equal talent and equally likely to be chosen.

Page 90: The computations are 56.87 × 895 ÷ 285.94 + 715 × 285.94 ÷ 715 + 56.87 × 715 ÷ 895 + 285.94 × 895 = . This process gives you $551 924.07, which is only 3 cents off the true answer.

Page 96: The likelihood of making any specific number of correct predictions were figured out with a standard binomial distribution formula. Here are the formula results.

Correct Predictions	Probability	Approximate Odds
0	.348 678 3	1 out of 3
1	.387 420 4	1 out of 3
2	.193 210 2	1 out of 5
3	.057 395 6	1 out of 20
4	.011 160 2	1 out of 100

5	.001 488	1 out of 750
6	.000 137 7	1 out of 7 000
7	.000 008 748	1 out of 100 000
8	.000 000 364 5	1 out of 3 million
9	.000 000 009	1 out of 100 million
10	.000 000 000 1	1 out of 10 billion

Page 100 The process may be just a bit different on your calculator, depending on what keystrokes store a number in memory. Using M+ is one way to show that the number on the display gets stored in memory—but you can do whatever process adds the display to memory. The sum of the first series is keyed: .5 M+ × = M+ = M+ = M+ ... until the numbers on the display get very small, or go to zero. The sum of $1/2 + (1/2)^2 + (1/2)^3 + \ldots$ is .9999999, and so the limit is obviously 1. For 1/3 the limit is .5, and for 1/5 the limit of the sum is .25.

Page 101 The solution involves only two memory keys— MR, which recalls memory to the display, and M+, which adds the display to the memory. If you have a memory but it functions with different keys, you can use this solution to make up your own.

Begin by setting up your calculator, with 48 M+ and then keying in 33. The solution is:

Keystrokes:	–	MR	=	M+	–	MR	=	–	–	–	–
Display shows:	33	48	–15	–15	–15	33	–48	–48	0	48
Memory has:	48	48	48	33	33	33	33	33	33	33

If your calculator doesn't have a constant add or subtract key, you may have to stop at the final = sign, with the negative number on your display.

Page 102 The keystrokes are 1 M+ ÷ 1 = M+ ÷ 2 = M+ ÷ 3 = M+ ÷ 4 = M+ ... The answer you get on your calculator should be close to 2.718 281 828 459 045, the value of *e* to 15 decimal places.

Finding the term e^x, is quite similar—just use *x* as your constant. To find e^2, for example, key in: 1 M+ × 2 = M+ × 2 ÷ 2 = M+ × 2 ÷ 3 = M+ × 2 ÷ 4 = M+ ... The answer to 12 decimal places is 7.389 056 098 930.

Page 103 One puzzle book gives the answer as 18 446 744 073 709 551 615 grains of wheat. But my calculator gives a slightly different answer. Here's how. First put the smallest number possible into the calculator—.000 000 1. Then multiply by 2 until it almost overloads—that's 49 times. Now divide by 10 000 000. At this point my calculator reads 5.629 498. Add this to the memory—all the numbers before now were too small to even worry about. Multiply by 2, adding the product to the memory every time you push the = key. Finally, when you have multiplied a total of 63 times by two, stop. That's how many grains of wheat there are on the 64th square of the chessboard. At this point your memory should total 184 461.74. But in getting the total we divided by 10 000 000 twice—once at the beginning and once at step 49. So the answer is 184 461.74 × 10 000 000 × 10 000 000, or 18 446 174 000 000 000 000 grains of wheat. That's close enough to the answer not to worry about.

Page 104: The square root of 2 is 1.414 213 562 373, to 12 decimal places. Your calculator will give it to you by doing this process: 2 ÷ = = + 2= ÷ = = + 2 = ÷ = = ... continuing until the numbers don't change much every time you add another 2 and divide twice. Then add 1.

The square root of 3 is 1.732 050 8. Use the process above to see if it works with 3.

Page 106: The limit of $1 \div n$ as *n* gets infinitely large is zero.

The largest number my calculator shows an answer to is 1 ÷ 9 999 999. After that, the calculator rounds the answer to zero, even though that isn't the true answer.

The limit of $1 \div n$ as n gets infinitely small is infinitely large.

Page 107: The limit of $n + 40 \div n$ is 1, as n gets larger. The larger n becomes, the more insignificant the 40 becomes, so the term approaches n/n, which is 1. The limit of $n + 40 \div n$ as n approaches 1 is 41. To see this, just do .9999 + 40 ÷ .9999 = , and do it again with .999 999, and so on.

The limit of $(17 \times n + 4) - n$ as n becomes very large is 17. This becomes very clear if you use 999 999 for n, since the answer is 17.000 004. The more 9's you add, the closer the answer approaches 17.